ACHIEVE FINANCIAL VICTORY

7 Ways to Win with Your Money

ACHIEVE FINANCIAL VICTORY

7 Ways to Win with Your Money

VANESSA LINDLEY

Lindley Consulting Group, LLC
New York

Book Title: Achieve Financial Victory: 7 Ways to Win With Your Money

ISBN: 978-0-578-57465-3

Printed in the United States of America

DEDICATION

I dedicate this workbook to:

My two late grandmothers, Ora Lee Warrick and Beatrice Alston where I first learned critical budgeting skills and many financial lessons. Grandma Ora Lee was able to feed a large family on a limited budget; the other taught me about property ownership, insurance, and multiple streams of income. Grandma "Bea" worked and owned the building we lived and collected rent from the tenants. The most important lesson both of my grandmothers taught me was about faith.

My late mother, Bernadette Wilson, who taught me about generosity and caring for, and loving, those in need.

My father, Walter Alston, who taught me the spirit of entrepreneurship and "charting your own path."

My husband, Marcos, who believes in me and supports me on this journey.

My daughters, Madison, Kennedy, and Chloe, who I hope to inspire.

My bonus mom, Carmen, sisters, brothers, aunts, uncles, cousins, nephews, and niece for their continued love and support.

My high school guidance counsellor, Earnstine Lannigan, who stood in the gap.

My sister-circle, WWP and all those in the group chat and texts cheering me on.

My National Urban League, NeighborWorks America, Jack and Jill of America, Goldman Sachs 10K Small Business families, New Dorp H.S., Binghamton University and Union Theological Seminary who were critical in my journey.

All of my friends, colleagues and clients who ever fed into me, believed in me, encouraged, and supported me. There are too many to name.

God almighty that I promised I would live in my purpose the best I could!

CONTENTS

STEP 5: MANAGING FINANCES AND FAMILY........................85

STEP 6: PROTECTING ASSETS...95

INTRODUCTION

This workbook offers seven strategies to help you achieve victory over your finances. It provides information that is informative, reflective, and action-oriented. The questions asked throughout the book are similar to those that a financial coach would ask you. Take your time to answer all of the questions and reflect upon your answers. Complete the worksheets, be as detailed as you can, and ultimately, take action on each applicable step. There are also blank pages throughout the book to journal or record anything that comes to your mind while you are working through the book.

It is important to note that the steps are not linear, but it can be beneficial to start from the first step and proceed in order to ensure you obtain a full scope of the lessons. Ultimately, the choice is yours—you can begin on the step that you feel is most important to you at this time on your financial journey. As you continue to progress on your journey to financial victory, there may be times when you will need to revisit a step. This is part of the process.

Achieving victory over your finances is a journey; change will not happen overnight. Be patient with the process, but also be diligent with your intentions and actions. **Victory is yours!**

Legal Disclaimer

The content in this workbook is general financial information. I strive to present the most accurate information. This not financial or legal advice. There are references to third-party resources and content. I do not endorse or guarantee the accuracy of the third-party information. All references to financial products and services are presented without warranty.

STEP 1

SETTING AND ACHIEVING FINANCIAL GOALS

"Without a vision, my people will perish..."
– Proverbs 29:18

Vanessa Lindley

SETTING AND ACHIEVING FINANCIAL GOALS

Goal setting is a critical step in achieving financial victory. Setting goals gives you focus, triggers action, allows you to measure progress, helps you overcome procrastination, and keeps you motivated.

One key is to make sure you set SMART goals: (S)pecific, (M)easurable, (A)ctionable, (R)ealistic and (T)ime-sensitive. For example, it will be difficult to reach a goal to "save more money" or to "get out of debt" because these two goals as stated have no target. They are neither quantifiable nor do they have a start or finish. So, your target is vague, and your actions will not have a focus.

An example of a SMART goal would be: "I want to pay off my $5,000 Visa bill in two years, by cutting off cable T.V. and automating the $200 payment to VISA each month." This goal as stated indicates the specific target ($5,000 Visa bill); you can measure progress by the monthly $200 payments as it states the action and has a deadline (two years), which makes it time-sensitive. The only questions you would have to answer if this was your goal are: is this a realistic goal? Would I have to cut off my cable T.V.? Do I actually have the $200 in my budget? But for the sake of this example, you should get the idea. Keep in mind that to make a goal realistic, you may have to adjust the amount of the payment amount or the time-frame. You may also have to adjust the actions that will provide the money needed to reach the goal (e.g., earning more income or spending less).

Once you set your goal, the next step to achieve financial victory is to make sure this is something you really want to do. To address this matter effectively, you have to start with "why?" Why is the financial goal important to you? What is your motivation for reaching this goal? How will your life be different if you achieved this goal? What would your life look like? To begin the process, let us start broad:

- What kind of life do you want? (Consider all areas of life.)

- What is important to you in your life? What do you value?

- What does financial success look like to you?

- Why is this important to you? How will your life be different or better?

DREAM BIG!

My biggest money goal or financial dream is:

Turn your goal into a SMART goal:

S—specific:

M—measurable:

A—actionable:

R—realistic:

T—time-bound:

This goal is important because:

If I achieved this goal:

Other financial goals to consider:

I would feel secure if I had $_____in my bank account.

I would like to earn $_____ annually.

I would like to retire with $_____ saved in order to:

Investing in my financial goals would mean spending more money on:

...and spending less money on:

Reaching financial goals requires focus and attention and may also require support and accountability, but it is possible! No matter where you are starting, victory is possible!

PLANNING TO WIN

Planning is the next step toward achieving your financial goals. You must treat your household economy like a business. You should be forecasting, planning, tracking, and making adjustments regularly. Many people do not like the word "budget"; it reminds them of a diet and feels restrictive. So, let us use the phrase "spending plan" instead. Having a spending plan gives you control of where your money goes. You decide. It is your plan! You achieve success, actually, by sticking to the plan.

As you move forward with your plans to win, you may want to consider these important questions of commitment: Are you a person of your word? Do you keep your promises to other people? Can you keep your promise to yourself to achieve the financial goals and plans you set for yourself? Answer these questions honestly and reflect on your level of commitment to others versus the commitment to yourself and make a decision to prioritize what is important to you.

Another great way to be successful in your spending plan is to make sure you account for ALL of your spending, big and small. Collect all of the necessary financial documents including pay stubs, employee benefit documents, social security statements, utility bills, mortgage statement, lease agreements, car notes, credit card statements, student loan documents, and any other pertinent financial documents.

> **SUCCESS TIP**
>
> "Use your after-tax income for your spending plan, because that is what you actually live off of."

When planning, most people focus on the "must haves" like housing, food, utilities, transportation, etc. But they, often, forget about the "nice to haves" that bring them joy and add value to their life like entertainment, gift giving, and coffee, to list a few. This may require that you track your spending for at least two weeks to know how much you actually spend on the "extras," and then commit to a spending plan. To achieve financial victory, you must include all spending in your spending plan.

Tools that can help you maintain your spending plan are spending plan worksheets and personal financial management platforms. Once you have established your spending plan, tracked your expenses, and selected the right tools, you may have to adjust your plan as you go along.

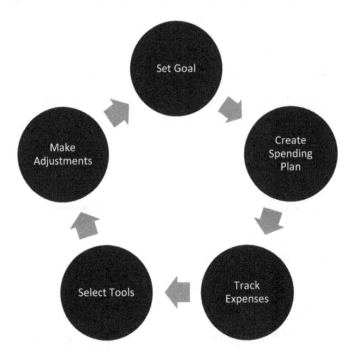

I recommend checking your plan weekly and making additional adjustments as necessary. Remember, this is your plan. Find ways to include your goals, needs and wants into your plan.

VICTORIOUS
SPENDING PLAN

Step 1: Identify Income Sources		
Source	**Expected per month**	**Actual per month**
After-tax income		
After-tax income from spouse's income		
Tips, bonuses, cash from hobbies		
Unemployment compensation		
Social Security or Supplemental Security Income		
Public assistance		
Child support		
Total Monthly Income		
Step 2: List Expenses		
Type	**Expected per month**	**Actual per month**
Savings for emergencies		
Rent/mortgage payment		
Utilities (electric, gas, oil)		
Mobile phone (all features)		
Home maintenance (repairs, cleaning, etc.)		
Groceries		
Car payment, maintenance, gasoline, parking		
Bus/train fare		
Insurance (car, homeowner's, life, health)		
Tuition or school-related fees		
Clothes or uniforms		
Childcare and extra-curricular activities		
Child support, alimony, spousal maintenance		
Pets (vet, grooming, food, kennel, etc.)		
Credit card payments (all)		
Union/organization dues		
Snacks and meals eaten out		
Personal (toiletries, hair, nails, etc.)		
Entertainment (movies, museums, happy hour)		
Charitable donations		
Savings for long-term goals		
Total Monthly Expenses		
Step 3: Compare Expected Income and Expenses		
Expected monthly income	$	
(minus) expected monthly expenses	-$	
Discretionary income	$	

What do you do When Your Discretionary Income is Negative?

If you find that your discretionary income is negative, you have three options: (1) spend less, (2) earn more, or (3) do both.

Let us look at some common traps and distractions that can lead to overspending and a negative cash flow.

COMMON TRAPS
AND DISTRACTIONS

Great, you have a spending plan, now what? What do you do when life kicks in? There are constant distractions that can take you off course from your plan. The key to victory is to identify what your common distractions are and devise a plan to be prepared and to overcome them. It is possible!

Many traps lure you in by offering convenience, easy access, and involve various influencers:

- Amazon "One Click"
- Store Ads
- Email Ads
- Social Media
- Social Media Ads
- TV/Radio Commercials
- Lack of Planning

- In Store Promotion
- Friends/Circle Influence
- Discounts
- Family Pressures
- Time Pressures
- Busy-ness

What are Some of Your Distractions?

1. What do you think your biggest challenge will be in sticking to your spending plan?

2. What are some common traps that you anticipate can take you off course?

3. What plans and strategies can you put in place now to help you prepare to overcome your common traps and distractions?

SPENDING DRIPS

Many people think they cannot afford to cut anything from their regular expenses. Yet, upon close analysis, they discover they have "spending drips," or expenses that zap money from their budgets without them really noticing, or without adding a lot of value to their lives. They are like a leaking faucet or pipe; they may be small drips, but they can cost you money and/or cause major damage over time. They are often incidental items that seem small in the moment but add up over time.

Potential Spending Drips

- Eating dinner out/ordering
- Cable TV
- Monthly subscriptions
- Amazon Prime orders

- Lunch/brunch
- Bank/late fees
- Uber/Lyft/Car service
- Impulse online/in-store purchases

What are Some of Your Spending Drips?

Finding Potential Spending Drips				
A. Item	**B. Cost of Item**	**C. Number of Items Purchased Per Month**	**D. Cost Per Month (BxC)**	**E. Cost Per Year (Dx12)**
Eating dinner out/ordering				
Cable TV				
Monthly subscriptions				
Manicures/pedicures				
Movies/Shows				
Parking tickets				
Cell phone plan				
New clothes/shoes				
Drinks/ night out				
Lunch/brunch				
Lottery tickets				
Bank fees				
Late fees on bills				
Impulse buys at store/online				
Bottled water				
Gifts				
Other:				

If you were not spending your money on _____ you could use it to help accomplish which of your short-term or long-term goals?

If you are not sure what your spending drips are, track your purchases for a week or two or review your bank and/or credit card statements. If you, primarily, use debit or credit cards, your statements will tell a story about your spending. See **"Ways to Track Your Spending"** and the **"Daily Cash Flow Tracker"** in the next section for help in this area.

WAYS TO TRACK YOUR SPENDING

Tracking Method	Instructions
Bills and Receipts	Save all receipts and bills and add them up at the end of the week or month. Gather information (bills or receipts) on irregular, expected expenses and convert them to monthly amounts. Estimate any expenses you are unable to track.
Notebook or Calendar	Get a notebook or calendar and write down everything you spend. Keep a thorough record, add up expenditures and then review them at the end of the week or month to see where overspending might be happening.
Bank and Credit Card Statements	Take the time to look closely at your bank and credit card statements to see where you are spending. Observe and calculate patterns.
"Daily Cash Flow Tracker"	Find a form you like online to track your daily expenses and spending method, such as the Daily Cash Flow Tracker (below).
Online or Mobile App	There are a variety of online or mobile apps. You can search online for "Personal Financial Management Platforms" or "spending tracking tools" to learn about different options.
Expense or Budget Worksheet	Use the spending plan worksheet above to keep track of your monthly totals and see where you spend money each month. There are also many options available online.

Daily CASH FLOW TRACKER

DATE	DESCRIPTION	CATEGORY	AMOUNT	CASH	CREDIT	DEBIT	NEED	WANT
				☐	☐	☐	☐	☐
				☐	☐	☐	☐	☐
				☐	☐	☐	☐	☐
				☐	☐	☐	☐	☐
				☐	☐	☐	☐	☐
				☐	☐	☐	☐	☐
				☐	☐	☐	☐	☐
				☐	☐	☐	☐	☐
				☐	☐	☐	☐	☐
				☐	☐	☐	☐	☐
				☐	☐	☐	☐	☐
				☐	☐	☐	☐	☐
				☐	☐	☐	☐	☐
				☐	☐	☐	☐	☐
				☐	☐	☐	☐	☐
				☐	☐	☐	☐	☐
				☐	☐	☐	☐	☐
				☐	☐	☐	☐	☐
				☐	☐	☐	☐	☐
				☐	☐	☐	☐	☐

Spending Drip Alternatives

I have found that not all items that we spend money on bring us pleasure or make our lives easier. A good thing to do is assess the cost of the item and the value it brings, then consider alternatives to that item as a way to save money, and, potentially, add more value to your life.

I remember at one point I felt like I "needed" to get a manicure and pedicure at least twice a month. I remember justifying these items, because I am a businessperson. I felt like I needed to look presentable (although, no one saw my toes in the winter). After having children, I added the "need" to pamper myself, because I deserved it. After all, I am a working Mom!

After a while, I started to assess how I felt when I was getting my manicures/pedicures. I realized I was stressed out! It was ANOTHER thing on my calendar, another thing TO DO. If the polish chipped on my nails in between appointments I felt stress, because I did not have time to go back and did not really want to spend the money.

When my children were about three, four, and five, they started wanting to play dress up and make up. So, I started painting their nails with "play" nail polish, and I started painting mine with real nail polish and it felt good! It became a stress reliever and something fun to do with my daughters. Who knew? I was still able to honor my value of "personal appearance" while having fun with my daughters and saving money.

> **COACH QUESTION:**
>
> *"What are you spending money on that is costing you money and not bringing you real happiness?*

Assess the things that you are doing and spending money on and determine for yourself what is working for you, what's not, and what alternatives you can do to honor your values, enjoy life, and reach your goals. Keep in mind the cost may be more than money, it may be time, added stress or pressure. Remember, once you have calculated the cost, you must take action! You can achieve victory in this area!

STEP 2

EXPLORING YOUR MONEY HABITS AND BELIEFS

"For the love of money is a root of all evil."
– 1Timothy 6:10

EXPLORING YOUR
MONEY HABITS AND BELIEFS

Your many life experiences affect your unconscious mind, which impacts what you think, what you believe, and what you do. Your beliefs affect your habits and your habits affect your finances. Becoming aware of your beliefs and habits is important to ensure they are in alignment with your goals and values.

So, where do these "unconscious money habits and beliefs" come from? They come from many sources like your family, upbringing, culture, faith, education, and personal experiences.

The life-changing event that had a major impact on my money habits and beliefs occurred when I was 12 years old. My mother, sister, and I were evicted from our apartment. This was such a shock to me. Up until that point it felt like we had it all. We had birthday parties, toys, the latest clothing, plenty of food and Christmas was always over the top. How could we now be homeless? My sister and I went from having our own room to sharing a room with our cousins over the several years when we lived with our grandmother.

This experience created a sense of *"financial insecurity"* in me. I have always felt vulnerable if I did not have a certain amount of emergency savings or a safety net. Unconsciously, I am worried about the possibilities of a financial disruption in my life or being displaced. Whether this will happen is irrelevant; but the thoughts manifest in my behaviors. I tend to play it safe with my finances. If my bank account gets low, I get stressed. The reality is, it is always good to have an emergency savings. (But) I had to realize that I was limiting some of my experiences based on an event that occurred when I was a child.

Your community and culture also influence your money habits and beliefs. This could be related to your ethnicity, geography, affinity, etc. Think about the things you do because that is what "we" do. "We" can be your family, your country, your neighborhood, your friends, your profession, etc. For example, many people are trying to keep up with "the Joneses." After the financial crisis I remember seeing a bumper sticker that said, "The Joneses are broke!" This was a way to let people know that things do not always appear as they seem, so it is important to stop trying to emulate other people as that could cause you to go broke.

Recognize that your environment and surroundings have an effect on you. These include who you hang out with, work with, go to school with, worship with, what you hear on the radio or read in the newspaper or magazine, and what you see on TV or social media; they all affect how you behave with your money.

I was fortunate to begin my career in a financial services company, so I was influenced by my environment and learned about money early. I bought my first house by the time I was 30 and have owned four properties. I own stocks, mutual funds, and life insurance, some of which I have owned since I was 21.

We live in a society that has adopted a **culture of "conspicuous consumption."** We can never have enough; everything is on sale; more is better than enough. This culture pervades everything we do and everywhere we go. Even our government encourages spending to "help the economy." You have to be mindful not to risk **your personal economy** by being sucked into the larger culture. Being conscious of your spending choices and intentional about your spending can help you achieve financial victory!

YOUR RELATIONSHIP WITH MONEY

Healthy Money Relationship

Financial decisions and behaviors are often based on a set of unconscious beliefs or **money scripts**. These scripts are developed concerning money and life and may be inaccurate, incomplete, or rooted in painful circumstances from the past. Following money scripts could cause some people to become stuck in financial chaos and struggle regardless of income or assets.

Common Money Scripts[1]

"Money is bad... the root of all evil."

"Money is unimportant."

"More is better."

"God will provide."

"I don't deserve money."

"I don't make enough."

"There will never be enough."

"More money will make things better"

"The rich obtained their money dishonestly"

These scripts can lead to self-defeating behaviors, sabotaging your financial goals and dreams.

---

[1] Adapted from Brad and Ted Klontz, Facilitating Financial Health

Creating a Healthy Relationship with Money is Emotional Work, not Financial Work, and Often Involves the Following Stages of Transformation:

1. Coming out of denial and identifying money scripts
2. Exploring and healing repressed emotions around the most deep- rooted scripts
3. Acquiring new information
4. Re-scripting your thoughts
5. Envisioning the future (what would I gain?)
6. Taking action

Why Understanding Your Relationship with Money is Important?

- Everyone has a relationship with money.
- It is one of the longest relationships you will have in your life.
- Many people have had negative relationships with money, resulting in negative behaviors.
- Some people have unresolved feelings about money and act in self-defeating ways and/or experience a lot of financial stress.
- Usually, beliefs are unconscious, and you can be "controlled" by them.
- Many people carry significant shame around the topic of money from having too much or too little.
- Achieving your financial goals, and financial victory can help change your mind set about money.

Re-scripting Thoughts About Money

"You can never have enough money"

Alternative thoughts:

- People could find themselves in a financial situation where there is not enough money.

- There are financial situations where there is enough money.

- Sometimes it is perceived that there is not enough money when there actually is.

- There are some circumstances where there is too much.

> **WHAT COULD FINANCIAL VICTORY LOOK LIKE?**
>
> *Abundance*
> *Clarity*
> *Authenticity*

COMMON FINANCIAL HABITS THAT PREVENT WEALTH ACCUMULATION

- **Not budgeting or tracking spending**. Many people do not have a budget. They do not plan or monitor spending, and thus do not know how much they spend on food, clothing, and entertainment or whether they would be able to reach their financial goals. Having a budget and organized tracking system can help with financial goal accomplishment, on-time bill payments, debt reduction, and saving. VICTORY IS POSSIBLE!

- **Not living within your means.** People are able to spend more than their household income and not save, primarily by borrowing. A common outcome for people who are overspending is credit card debt. You could be overspending for a variety of reasons—overconsumption, lack of planning and/or the high cost of living. Many families are struggling with high costs for rental housing, healthcare, childcare and transportation. In addition, consumerism is deeply rooted in the economic structure. Pervasive marketing and advertising pressures people to spend, especially on non-essentials. VICTORY IS POSSIBLE!

- **Not paying bills on time.** Some people have trouble keeping up with monthly expenses and bills. You might not be paying bills on time and/or occasionally overdrawing your accounts. Late payments could be due to unpredictable income, overspending or not being organized. This can result in excessive fees, financial hardships, negative debt, and/or an impaired credit history. VICTORY IS POSSIBLE!

- **Having high debt.** Borrowing has always played a role in American's lives—not only as a means of instant gratification, but also as a strategy for survival and a tool for economic advancement. As the cost of living has increased for everything from housing to healthcare, the average amount of debt per household has grown rapidly—from credit cards, mortgages, student loans, non-bank loans and other sources. VICTORY IS POSSIBLE!

- Many households end up borrowing money (formally or informally) when an unforeseen crisis occurs. The additional debt these households accumulate affects their ability to save. An ongoing lack of savings makes them more likely to resort to more borrowing when future crises occur. The result is an ongoing cycle of financial vulnerability. People with debt problems often feel overwhelmed and powerless. VICTORY IS POSSIBLE!

- **Having high student loan debt.** With rising costs and shrinking government support for higher education, people have been taking on vast amounts of debt to finance their college education. Many people are also pursuing advanced or specialized (doctor, legal, PhD) degrees. High student loan debt can have serious consequences, causing trouble with making ends meet and delays in major life events like buying a home, getting married or having children. We'll discuss in Step 3 in the section on minimizing debt, you need to calculate the Return on Investment (ROI) on the investment in education. VICTORY IS POSSIBLE!

Assessing Your Money Habits and Beliefs

1. Where do your money habits and beliefs come from? What has been most influential (e.g., Upbringing/Family, Culture, Faith, Personal Experiences, Education)?

2. What role did money play in your home growing up? What lessons did learn about money, or not? How have those experiences shaped your feelings and experiences around money as an adult? Write your "money belief birth" story.

3. Are your habits and beliefs helping you reach your goals? Explain how or why not.

4. What can you do to begin to change the money habits and beliefs that are not serving/ helping you?

EMOTIONAL INTELLIGENCE AND MONEY

Emotional intelligence is the capacity to be aware of, control and express your emotions, and as a result manage interpersonal relationships thoughtfully and empathetically. Emotional intelligence is important for both personal and professional success. As it relates to money, many of your spending choices are related to your emotions. According to the Oxford dictionary, emotion is "a natural instinctive state of mind deriving from one's circumstances, mood, or relationships with others." The goal is to become self-aware and then intentional about spending.

Think About Some Items You Purchased in the Last 30 Days:

1. What were the items? How much did they cost?

2. What was your mood? Were you sad, tired, lonely, depressed, happy, excited, stressed?

3. What were you thinking about? Or were you not thinking?

If this is an area where you need to take control, you could benefit from using a "Financial Mood Journal" to track your spending behaviour and record your emotions and state of mind when making purchases. You would track the item you purchase, the cost, the date, day, and time you purchased the item and lastly, the mood, thoughts, or emotions you were experiencing at the time. I recommend tracking for a couple of weeks to notice patterns and trends.

Financial Mood Journal			
Item Purchased	**Cost**	**Day of the week & Date** (ex. Monday, June 19)	**Emotion, mood, thoughts, state of mind**

Financial Mood Journal

Item Purchased	Cost	Day of the week & Date (ex. Monday, June 19)	Emotion, mood, thoughts, state of mind

Financial Mood Journal			
Item Purchased	Cost	Day of the week & Date (ex. Monday, June 19)	Emotion, mood, thoughts, state of mind

Five Ways to Become Aware, Intentional, and Take Control Over Your Money

1. **Know What Makes You Happy.** As stated in step one, assessing and knowing what you value and what makes you happy can help you be in control of your money. Being aware of your emotions can also help you focus your time and resources on providing yourself with more of the things that make you happy and achieve your financial goals.

2. **Be a Trend Setter (Avoid Peer Pressure).** Being self-aware and in control can help you avoid the influence of family, friends, co-workers or others with regards to the way they spend their money. in being self-aware, you will be able to distinguish your needs and wants from that of others and better able to resist the pressure of criticism that may come from doing things differently. This may be challenging in the beginning, but once you begin to reach your financial goals, you will feel better and may start a new trend for your circle.

3. **Be a Goal Getter (Delay Gratification).** By identifying what you want in life and focusing on your goals as you did in step one, it will become easier for you to deny yourself of immediate rewards. You will be able to see the benefit and greater satisfaction of waiting to reach your goal. Knowing what you want and striving to achieve it gives your life purpose, meaning, and fulfilment. You will see victory on the horizon!

4. **Enjoy the Path to Victory.** Finding ways to reward yourself on your journey to financial victory will aide in our success. People who are more self-aware recognize the small pleasures that cost little but are very satisfying help along the way to achieving larger and better goals. Knowing what really makes you happy allows you to treat yourself along the way, and in turn will motivate you to keep moving towards

larger goals. Whatever your income level, make the most of it by finding what gives you the most satisfaction within your budget. If you're unable to afford what you want at this time, you can substitute it for something less expensive which will still offer some satisfaction. Be creative and flexible in finding affordable ways to reward yourself in ways that are truly satisfying to you.

5. **Practice Gratitude.** When you are in a state of gratitude for what you have, you are more likely to find contentment when you're able to afford to buy more. You will be able to break the cycle of spending on small things that only bring temporary satisfaction. When you're discontented with what you have, you may fall into the trap of trying to "keep up with the Joneses," buying things you may not really want or need. When you are unhappy and feeling dissatisfied, you can end up rushing into purchases with the hope and belief that you will be happier or be better when you find the latest and shiniest object. This illusive cycle can leave you broke. Take inventory of your life, what brings you true joy, your wants and needs and be grateful for where you are on this journey and be ready for the victory!

TRANSFORMING YOUR RELATIONSHIP WITH MONEY

Your relationship with money is one of the longest relationships you will have in your life, yet you may not always give this idea the attention it needs to flourish. Bringing consciousness to your financial affairs and engaging in a mindset of growth and power can transform your financial life. Below are "Ten Mindful Money Habits to Adopt" to help you get started. A financial coach can help you go deeper and recognize your money mindset and work with you to help you on your path to financial success. *Financial victory is possible!*

> *To further this work, you may benefit from working with a financial coach.*

10 Mindful Money Habits to Adopt

1. **Schedule Time with Your Money**—Put an alert on your calendar to check your accounts daily.

2. **Adopt a Spending Mantra**— (E.g., "I will only spurge on a pair of shoes after I've paid all my bills and met my savings goals").

3. **Automate Your Savings**—Set up an automatic transfer from your pay check to your bank account.

4. **Get an Accountability Partner**—Share your money goal with a friend or hire a financial coach.

5. **Tell Yourself You Deserve More**—Not another dinner, gadget, or clothing item, but to be safe if you lose your job, to be free of bad debt, and to save for something that will truly make you happy. The next time you are tempted to spend, ask yourself: Do I deserve this $40 candle/$25 dinner/$150 pair of sneakers, or do I deserve more?

6. **Make a List**—Many people over spend on groceries, so make a list on your phone, send an email to yourself or on a pad.

7. **Put Your Overspending on Ice**—Literally freeze your credit cards for 2-3 months to break the habit and remove overdraft protection from your debit cards.

8. **Let a Bad Day Be a Blip**—Do not beat yourself up, start over the next day.

9. **Build a 15-Minute Buffer**—When you feel a financially irresponsible impulse, immediately do something else to take your mind off of it.

10. **Use Super Savings Strategies**—Set up separate savings accounts, specifically, to save for your major financial goals. This will help you focus and track your progress.

STEP 3

MAXIMIZING CREDIT AND MINIMIZING DEBT

"The rich rule over the poor,
and the borrower is servant to the lender."
— Proverbs 22:7

MAXIMIZING CREDIT

In our current economic system, credit is an important factor in your financial life and integral part of financial opportunities. The higher your credit score(s), the more likely you are to qualify for loans and credit cards at lower interest rates and the most favorable terms, which will in turn will save you money. Additionally, your credit history can affect employment, housing, insurance, and the ability to borrow in the future. Any of these can affect your overall livelihood.

Why Is Credit Important?

- Housing
- Employment
- Interest rate
- Insurance
- Costs of goods and services

- Ability to borrow
- Home ownership
- Car/Truck
- Start or grow a business
- Higher education

This may seem unfair, but your credit history can be seen as an indication of your character. You are borrowing money from various entities and being judged on how you pay it back. It is your reputation from all creditors in one place.

In some instances, you may not have enough credit history to get a loan, which seems counter-intuitive. It seems as if never taking out loans or taking out very few would be a good thing, but creditors need to see that when you borrow money you will pay it back.

We are being affected by our culture of debt, AND **we are still responsible for our actions.**

What Makes up a Credit Score?

The two largest percentages of your credit score are your payment history (35%) and how much you owe (30%). Therefore, you must make every effort to pay your bills on time and pay off debt and keep your outstanding debt as low as possible.

The next area is the length of credit history, which makes up 15% of your score. You want to keep credit lines open as long as you can. As long as there are no annual fees, do not close unused credit cards. Closing accounts may increase your credit utilization ratio. Owing the same amount spread out over fewer open accounts may lower your credit scores.

The last two areas, new credit and credit mix, each make up 10% of your score. Look at how much new credit you are applying for and the different types of credit you have. Only apply for new credit when you need to, because opening a new credit card can increase your overall credit limit, but each time you apply for credit it creates a hard inquiry on your credit report. Too many hard inquiries can negatively impact your credit score, though this effect will fade over time. When shopping for a car loan or home loan, you want attempt to complete all applications within one or two weeks. As it pertains to credit mix, if you mostly have retail credit cards, and no other types of debt, this may affect your credit negatively.

While there is no uniform algorithm employed by all lenders or other financial companies to compute the scores, they all generally use the above factors. One of the most common scoring models used, amongst other, is FICO and the score ranges from 300 to 850. See chart below on how the scores are viewed from very poor to excellent.

You are entitled to one free credit report per year from each of the three major credit bureaus (TransUnion, Equifax, and Experian) on annualcreditreport.com. If you have never seen your score or do not check it regularly (at least twice a year), you are leaving yourself at risk. If you find any errors on any of the reports, you must dispute them. Incorrect information on your credit reports could drag your scores down. Verify that the accounts listed on your reports are correct.

Establishing Credit

If you do not have enough credit history, and need to establish credit or build a history, there are several things you can do.

1. **Secured card or secured loan**. You can apply for a secured credit card or secured loan, which is backed by your own money. They are usually tied to a savings account, and the limit on the card or loan is typically the amount in the bank account or a percentage of it. Like a regular credit card or loan, you build credit by keeping your balance low or at

zero and paying on time every month. Make sure the lender is willing to report your history to the credit reporting companies or willing to convert the account to a traditional credit card after a certain period of time.

2. **You can become an authorized user on someone else's account**. With these types of accounts, you are responsible for repaying charges on the card or loan, and so is the other account holder. If you don't repay money borrowed on a joint account or pay late, the joint cardholder will have to, or both parties' credit will be negatively affected.

3. **Auto installment loan**. Auto loans are among the easiest types of loans to obtain, although the interest rate and terms can vary greatly. Shop around for the best deal and ask friends for referrals.

4. **Non-traditional credit lines**. Rental and utility payment history can be proof of your ability to pay bills on time. These don't typically appear on a credit report, unless you don't pay them, and the service provider sends the delinquent amount to a collection agency or files suit against you to recover the past due amount. You can now ask your landlord to report your positive payment history to the credit bureaus and they will include it on your credit report.

MINIMIZING DEBT

I believe there are different types of debt. There is good debt, bad debt, and tolerable debt. Good debt usually gives you a return on your investment (ROI), meaning you are able to make money off of the investment you used the loan to for. Examples include loans for inventory for a business or to purchase real estate, which can provide cash flow and/or increase your overall net worth. Bad debt is the type of debt used to purchase things that lose value like clothing, electronics, etc. It is better to save for these items and pay cash. Tolerable debt is debt used for items that may or may not increase in value, like a home mortgage.

In general, no more than 20% of your net (after-tax) income should be paid to consumer debt payments (credit cards, student loans). When looking at your debt, remember to consider the amount you borrowed along with the interest on the debt. Keep in mind that while you are paying down your debt, you are being charged interest on the remaining balance. **Calculate how much you can afford on a monthly basis to give you a benchmark.**

Yearly income after taxes and deductions = $_____

Monthly income: $_____ *(Yearly income ÷ 12)*

Amount of consumer debt per month that I should not exceed is:
$_____ *(Monthly net income x 0.20)*

I can afford to pay no more than $_____ per month, including interest charges.

Now that you have a pretty good idea of the amount of consumer debt you can manage on a monthly basis, you can begin making adjustments to your spending plan.

A word of caution: If your current debt level is below what you can afford to pay each month, do not feel compelled to go on a spending spree! Instead, congratulate yourself on living below your means. Your lower debt level can mean more freedom to reach your long-term goals sooner. Also, the 20% rule of thumb is general and may not apply to you. For example, if you live in an area with high housing costs, you may not be able to afford even 15% in consumer debt, because you have to use more of your money to pay your rent or mortgage.

"But I am way above 20%, what can I do?" Working with a **financial coach** can help you put together a debt reduction plan and **hold you accountable to your goals** of paying down your debt. You will have to be disciplined to not only pay your debts as planned, but also to avoid accumulating new debt.

As you are paying down your debt you should also be very intentional about establishing or continuing to build your emergency savings. One of the reasons people get into personal consumer debt is because they do not have an accumulated savings to cover the emergencies that come up in life (car repair, health insurance co-payment, etc.).

Below are a few debt reduction strategies to eliminate debt. But, before you choose a strategy, you need to calculate your total debt, interest rate and minimum payments, and determine whether the loan is providing a return on your investment (ROI) for all accounts. Then, select a strategy and rank the order in which you plan to pay them off.

DEBT REDUCTION WORKSHEET					
Account	Outstanding Balance	Interest Rate	Minimum Monthly Payment	ROI (Y/N)	Pay-Off Ranking
You can be debt free, believe it!					

Debt Reduction via the Snowball Strategy

To begin this method, make sure you have budgeted enough to cover the minimum monthly payment for every debt item you have and figure out how much extra you have in your budget to add to your debt reduction plan. Now, **arrange the debts by balance, from smallest to largest**. Disregard the interest rates.

Every month put the extra money you budgeted for paying off debt toward your smallest debt, even if other debts have higher interest. Once the smallest debt is repaid, take the entire amount you were paying toward it (monthly minimum plus your extra money), and start paying the next-smallest debt. Keep paying off debts, and then use all the freed-up money to pay the next debt in line.

For example, if you have a hospital bill for $1,500 that the hospital is allowing you to pay without interest, and two credit card bills for $4,000 at 22.9% interest and $2,500 at 18.9% interest, you would pay the hospital bill first. Yes, you would pay the interest-free debt before you pay the interest-bearing debt. This may seem counterintuitive, because it usually saves time and money to pay highest-interest debts first. Visualize a snowball starting small, rolling down a snowy hill and getting bigger as the snow accumulates on it. This is what this method does for you. The small victories early on can keep you motivated to stick with your plan, and you will see the amount you can pay get bigger and the debt eliminated.

As you consistently pay your bills on time, and begin to pay off your debts, your credit score should begin to increase. This could give an opportunity to find lower interest rates for your balances with high interest rates. You may also be able to transfer a credit card balance to a lower-rate card or find a debt consolidation loan.

Debt Reduction via the Avalanche Strategy

In the avalanche strategy, first you add up all the minimums required to pay on your debt, **ordered from the highest interest rates to lowest**, and then figure out how much extra you can pay beyond the total of your minimums.

For example, you have a hospital bill for $500, and the hospital is allowing you to pay it interest- free. You also have a credit card balance of $3,500 at 22.9% interest and another of $5,000 at 13.9%. The $3,500 credit card balance becomes your top priority, because it carries the highest interest rate. If you can put an extra $100 over your total minimums to pay off debt, it will go to that one until it is paid off. Once that is paid off, you then add that debt's minimum to the $100 extra and put the total toward the bill with the second-highest interest rate ($5,000 at 13.9%).

Continue paying off debts and rolling their minimums into the extra debt payment amount until all debts are paid off. Like an avalanche, which is a massive amount of snow, you till tackle your debts and pay them off quicker. By paying the largest interest first you will pay less in interest and save money.

Debt Reduction via the Snowflake Strategy

The snowflake method finds small day-to-day savings to help speed up your goal of being debt free. Like snowflakes, tiny payments made over time can have a huge impact. Remember snowflakes make up both snowballs and avalanches, and you can use this method with both strategies.

Both snowball and avalanche strategies use money you have committed in your budget to pay off debt. They are both a very focused method. But sometimes you come across "extra" money, like a rebate check. You can maximize either payoff strategy by using that "found" money to help get rid of your debt quicker.

Examples:

- Finding $5, $10, 20 in your clothes before taking them to the cleaners
- An unexpected rebate check
- Payments from extra work or side hustles
- Financial gifts for birthdays or holidays
- Jar of change

Regardless of which strategy you use, the key to eliminating debt is by creating a budget and sticking to it. There are online platforms and apps to help you implement your debt reduction strategies as well as non-profit debt management organizations. There are also credit repair programs if your credit is damaged. Make sure you do your research to find a reputable program.

Student Loan Debt

Many are burdened with student loan debt and are having to put off big life events like marriage and purchasing a home as a result. If you are in this position, you will have to approach paying down student loan debt with intention and focus. There are resources to help with student loan debt including special programs for loan forgiveness if you work in certain industries like non-profit organizations and income-based repayment plans.

Fifth Third Bank has a special program called Momentum that automatically rounds up your debit card purchases and applies it to your student loan balance. These smaller payments added to your regular student loan payments will help pay down your debt faster and save on interest.

Student Loans Resources

- Studentaid.ed.gov

- Studentloans.gov

- 53.com - Momentum

How is the burden of debt affecting your life?

How would your life be different if you did not have debt? Who would you be? What would you do?

What will you do to get a better handle on your debt?

What help do you need? (Contact us at vanessalindley.com)

FINANCIAL BEHAVIORS THAT AFFECT YOUR CREDIT AND DEBT

Some financial behaviors can work against your efforts to build your credit and be debt free. Here are some common mistakes and solutions:

1. **Not having and sticking to a budget.** A personal budget is the foundation for all aspects of money management. Planning and knowing how much you are spending and saving every month can put you in a better position to make sound decisions about how to maximize credit and how to minimize debt. As mentioned in step two, you must also manage your thoughts and emotions.

2. **Failure to protect yourself with an emergency savings.** Having an emergency savings allows you to be prepared for financial emergencies that come up like car repairs, home maintenance, healthcare costs, etc. Without having an emergency savings, you can be forced to rely on credit to cover these costs and put in you on a cycle of debt.

3. **Not understanding how much debt you can afford.** Calculate your debt-to-income ratio, which is all of your monthly debt obligations (including consumer debt and mortgages) divided by your gross income (before taxes are taken out). This will give you a benchmark on how creditors review your file when applying for things such as a mortgage. In general, a 43% debt-to-income ratio should be taken into consideration when taking on additional debt. There are online "debt-to-income" calculators to help you with this.

4. **Failing to shop around for high priced installment loans**. Some people spend more time pricing small appliances, electronics, clothing, and shoes than high ticket items like a mortgage or car loan. You should comparison shop for the best possible deal for these items, like any other. You should be looking for the lowest available interest rates, fees, and service charges.

5. **Failing to protect yourself from fraud.** Federal law protects consumers from some effects of credit fraud and many credit card companies have programs in place to reduce fraud. It is however good practice to protect yourself as well. Review your credit statements every month and monitor your credit report at least twice a year. Shred statements and receipts that have your account number on them, as well as any credit offers you receive in the mail. You can also opt out of pre-screened offers using optoutprescreen.com.

Credit can be a powerful tool to help you achieve your victory with your financial goals. It is important to understand how it works, how to build your credit and how to ensure your credit history always works for you. For example, when you first start out in business, your personal credit will be reviewed for business financing. In addition, credit can be used as leverage for business funding, real estate investments and more. In some instances, credit can give you more leverage than cash.

For example, let's say you have $200,000 to buy real estate property. If you used all cash you could only buy one property for $200K, but if you used a combination of cash and credit, you may be able to buy five properties at 20% down each ($40,000). Using debt allows you to purchase multiple properties that, if they each had equity in them, could increase your overall net worth. So, instead of putting all your money into one real estate property, debt gives you the chance to build your real estate portfolio.

I bought my first house in 2001 with 3% down because I had good credit, savings and investments in my 401K, and cash value in my life insurance policy. As I continued to build my real estate portfolio, I was able to purchase two additional properties with no money down. Although this is no longer common practice, at the time my credit score gave me these opportunities.

While credit algorithms and loan requirements may change over time, the practice of paying your bills on time and not overextending yourself in debt will put you in a position of power and open the door for opportunities.

STEP 4

SAVING, INVESTING AND WEALTH BUILDING

"Wealth gained hastily will dwindle,
but whoever gathers little by little will increase it."
– Proverbs 13:11

Vanessa Lindley

SAVING, INVESTING
AND WEALTH BUILDING

S aving and investing are the keys to creating generational wealth and building a lasting legacy. Saving is the first step to provide basic financial security. Long-term saving and investing strategies are necessary to secure your future income and reach financial goals.

Before you can invest, it is best to start the habit of saving at least 10% of your income or as much as you can. The easiest way to make saving a habit is to tie it to a goal and to automate it. Think about the goals you identified in step #1 and how you can set up savings accounts to help you achieve those goals. Having your savings come directly out of your pay check or account and go directly into a savings vehicle/ account that is hard to get to can help you reach those goals and build up savings. Lastly, sticking to your spending plan can also help ensure success in your saving.

A behavioural economic (study of human behaviors and money) tip is to set up designation goal savings account. So, separate accounts for each of your major savings goals. For example, if you had savings goals for emergency savings, a vacation, a holiday, and college, you would have four different accounts, labelled according to each goal. You would have to shop around for a bank or credit union that would not charge you a fee for each.

Why Is Saving Important to You?

Benefits of Saving

- Security

- Retirement

- Personal Financial Goal(s)

- Education (yours or your children)

- Generational Wealth

> **SAVING TIP**
>
> Set up designated goal accounts:
> - Emergency Savings
> - College Savings
> - Vacation
> - Holidays/Special Occasions

Saving Tips and Tools

- Automate savings—Direct deposit pay-checks, auto-transfer savings, payroll deduction into your bank, online bank, credit union or retirement accounts:

    o Chase, Citi, Fifth Third

    o National Credit Union Association—NCUA.gov

    o Community Development Financial Institution (CDFI) — OneUnited Bank, Liberty Bank and Trust Company

    o Online banking—SmartyPig.com

- Use automated savings apps that do the saving for you—Digit.com

- Participate in Saving/Lending Circles—Community-based saving programs. LendingCircle.org

- Save cash— "Mattress Money"

- Research bank interest rates—Bankrate.com

THE PAY YOURSELF FIRST FORMULA	
How Much of Your Income Should You Save? That Depends on Your Goals!	
Wealthy Enough to Retire Early	Pay yourself first at least 20% of your gross income.
Wealthy	Pay yourself first 15% to 20% of your gross income.
Upper Middle Class	Pay yourself first 10% to 15% of your gross income.
Middle Class	Pay yourself first 5% to 10% of your gross income.
Poor Mindset	Think about paying yourself first but do not actually do it.
Forever Broke	Do not pay yourself first spend more than you earn, borrow money you cannot payoff and live on credit card.

20 Ways to Save

1. Adjust cable, use streaming services

2. Do free activities – beach, parks, community festivals, library

3. Research your company and affiliate benefits for discounts and free services

4. Host a potluck game night

5. Clip coupons or download store apps for discounts

6. Reduce monthly subscriptions you hardly use

7. Pack lunch, snacks, and beverages for yourself or if you have children

8. Make coffee at home or use a reusable cup at your favorite shop for a discount

9. Buy in bulk items you use often

10. Install fluorescent bulbs

11. Lower temperature on water heater

12. Get a free energy audit from your utility company

13. Set thermostat to 68 degrees in the winter and 78 in the summer

14. Always do a full load of laundry—save money and the environment

15. Barter services—remember time is money

16. Repair running toilets and leaking faucets quickly

17. Borrow books and DVDs from the public library rather than renting or buying them

18. Eat out less—plan your meals

19. Take a vacation from spending for a week each month

20. Vacation at home this year

If after setting your goals, establishing your budget and tracking your spending, you find that you need to increase your income, here are some tips and strategies. Be sure to consider your values, lifestyle, and family structure before selecting one.

11 Strategies to Increase Your Income:

1. Start a home-based business and sell your work online—Etsy, Amazon, Shopify, UpWorks

2. Rent out an unused room in your house or rent space in your garage— Airbnb, SpareRoom

3. Set up a referral system for business partners, so you are paid a referral fee for all referrals

4. Become an "affiliate marketer" – promote products you like online and earn a commission on the sales that you make – Amazon, Shopify, Clickbank

5. Take a class for self-improvement or learn a new skill to increase your marketability for a raise or new contract opportunity

6. Sell your unwanted or unneeded stuff online – eBay, Amazon, consignment sites

7. Buy an investment property (or several) and rent it out

8. Take maximum advantage of your company's 401(k) or 403(B) retirement benefits

9. Take a second job in the evenings or weekends (count the cost of time and expenses vs. pay) – AriseWorkFromHome.com

10. Work with a tax preparer and see if you qualify for tax credits or deductions

11. Write a book and sell it online and in stores

Are there any strategies you would add to this list?

What strategies will you implement and by when?

Who will hold you accountable? How will you ask for accountability?

WEALTH AND NET WORTH

Wealth is different from income. Income is money you earn or receive from different sources (business, child support, dividends, etc.) Wealth is an accumulation of valuable assets and is usually a measure of your net worth. Net worth is the difference between what you own (assets) minus what you owe (liabilities). To calculate your net worth, add what you have in savings, investments, real estate and cash, and subtract any debts you owe.

For example, let's say you have a $350,000 house, a car worth $20,000, mutual funds worth $100,000, and $5,000 in a checking account. These assets would total 475,000, but if you owe $300,000 on your house, $14,000 on your car and have $60,000 in student loans, your net worth would be $101,000 ($475,000 in assets - $374,000 in liabilities).

Wealth Building Strategies

Wealth building takes strategy, planning and intention. It is best to have a diverse portfolio of assets and investments including cash, stocks, bonds, mutual funds, real estate, businesses, trusts, etc. If you are a beginner investor, it would be best to consult with a financial advisor or expert in the field.

To determine your net worth, you can use the net-worth calculator on the next page or find one online. List all of your assets and liabilities, then subtract the total liabilities from the total assets. The difference will be your net worth. If the number is positive, then you are in the "black". If the difference is negative, then you are in the "red". The goal is to be in the "black". If you're in the "red", you need to pay down your debts and reduce your liabilities. At the same time, you need to work on increasing your savings and investments and assets.

To be wealthy you have to have more assets than liabilities and be in the "black". I'll share some investing strategies and ways to build wealth next.

NET WORTH CALCULATOR

Name: **As of:**

Assets

Cash

Checking accounts	
Savings accounts	
CDs (certificates of deposit)	
Life Insurance (cash surrender value)	
Other case	
Total Cash	

Investments

Securities (stocks, bonds, mutual funds)	
Treasury Bills	
Other Investments	
Total Investments	

Property

Real estate (market value)	
Automobile (present value)	
Bullion (silver, gold, etc.)	
Jewelry, Art, and Collectibles	
Other Properties	
Total Property	

Retirement

Retirement Accounts (IRA, 401K)	
Employer Pension ($/month * 240)	
Social Security ($/month * 240)	
Other Assets	
Notes and Accounts Receivables	
Total Retirement	

Total Assets

Liabilities

Account Payable	
Auto Loan	
Credit Card Debt	
Consumer Loans or Instalments	
Loan on Life Insurance	
Real Estate Mortgages	
Student Loans	
Unpaid taxes	
Money Owed to Others Other liabilities	

Total Liabilities

Net Worth

INVESTING

In addition to creating wealth, investing can help offset the cost of inflation. The time value of money helps you to understand how the value of a dollar today will decline over time due to inflation (the rising costs of goods and services). For example, today you can purchase a latte for $4, in the future it may cost $6 and your $4 will not be able to purchase it. The only way to offset the loss of purchasing power over time is to invest in things that beat the cost of inflation.

When considering investing options, you want to consider the rate of growth as a percentage. If inflation ranges from 1% - 4%, you want to beat that rate in your investment choices. The chart below shows you a comparison of how investing $10,000 (10% of an annual household income of $100K) with different rates of return can accumulate growth. The major investment categories include stocks, bonds, mutual funds, business, and real estate.

Initial Investment = $10,000

Time	Rate of Growth					
(Years)	5%	6%	10%	11%	15%	20%
5	12,763	13,382	16,105	16,851	20,114	24,883
10	16,289	17,908	25,937	28,394	40,456	61,917
15	20,789	23,966	41,772	47,846	81,371	154,070
20	26,533	32,071	67,275	80,623	163,665	383,376
25	33,864	42,919	108,347	135,855	329,190	953,962
30	43,219	57,435	174,494	228,923	662,118	2,373,763
35	55,160	76,861	281,024	385,749	1,331,755	5,906,682
40	70,400	102,857	452,593	650,009	2,678,635	14,697,716

Types of Investments

Stocks—When you purchase stocks, you are purchasing a security or "shares" that gives you as the shareholder a share of ownership in the company. Stocks offer investors a potential for growth over the long term. Investors willing to hold stocks over long periods of time, say 15 years, generally have been rewarded with strong, positive returns. Keep in mind that stock prices move down as well as up. So, you can lose the money you invest in stocks as there is no guarantee that the company whose stock you hold will always do well.

Bonds—When you purchase bonds, you are basically lending money to a corporation or government entity. It is usually fixed income, meaning the interest rate on the return is a fixed amount. It is also usually a lower rate of return than stocks because it is a loan. A bond could be thought of as an I.O.U. between you, the lender, and the borrower (government or corporate that includes the details of the loan and its payments). Like any investment, it does not come without any risk, but tend to be more stable.

Mutual Funds—When you purchase a mutual fund, you are investing in a diversified portfolio of stocks, bonds, and other securities. A mutual fund is made up of a pool of money collected from many investors. The average mutual fund holds hundreds of different securities, which means mutual fund shareholders gain important diversification at a low price. Consider an investor who buys only Apple stock before the company has a bad quarter. She is at risk of losing a great deal of value because all of her dollars are tied to one company. On the other hand, if she bought shares of a mutual fund that happens to own some Apple stock when Apple has a bad quarter, she only loses a fraction as much because Apple is just a small part of the fund's portfolio. One consideration with mutual funds are the fees.

Exchange Traded Funds (ETF's) —An exchange-traded fund (ETF) is a collection of securities (stocks, commodities, bonds, or a mixture of investment types) that tracks an underlying index like the S&P 500. ETF share prices fluctuate all day as the ETF is bought and sold; as opposed to mutual funds that only trade once a day after the market closes. ETFs offer low expense ratios and fewer broker commissions than buying the stocks individually.

These types of investments can be bought from a variety of investment companies or brokerage houses. Some companies have minimum investment requirements, so you should shop around for the best company and best advisor within the company for you. Seek to work with someone who is willing to educate you on your options and partner with you on your goals.

Investment Companies:

- Merrill Lynch
- Edward Jones
- Fidelity
- Vanguard
- State Farm Insurance

For people who want to manage their own investments, there are many online platforms available. The fees are usually lower than working with an advisor and you are in control of your investments. If you choose this option, make sure you do your research on the companies, industries, environment, and risks. Lastly, make sure you are comfortable taking on the risks involved in managing your own investments. Because the initial investment amounts can be lower online, it is a great way for new investors to get their feet wet. Apps like StashInvest and Acorns actually invest based off your spending habits, so you can invest your spare change and lower your investing risk. This can also be a great way to start investing with your children.

Online Platforms:

- Sharebuilder.com
- Betterment.com
- Etrade.com
- StashInvest.com
- Acorns.com

Investing Trends

As an investor, you must be on the lookout for trends. Some are just that- trends. However, others turn out to be big payoffs. If we only focus on the bad stories like the Dot-com bubble or the real estate bubble, we will lose out on great opportunities. With proper research there is money that can be made in some of these seemingly trends. You have to know your risk tolerance and stay abreast of key indicators for success and failure of the particular investments.

Currently there is a boom in cryptocurrency, **blockchain** and CBD/Hemp products. Some people are fearful of cryptocurrency which is a digital asset exchanged on a decentralized ledger called blockchain. I know very technical, but what I want you to understand is not the technology, but the fact that this is the future of finance that must be embraced. Like the Dot-com bubble brought us the Internet, cryptocurrency is bringing us blockchain that will change the way we do business in many industries. Pay attention and learn about it.

The other trend to watch is the Cannabidiol (**CBD**) industry. CBD is derived from the cannabis plant and has an estimated industry potential of $22 billion. There are opportunities in this industry with everything from farming, retail, education, and supplies. As states continue to legalize the use of cannabis, the opportunities will continue to expand.

Some investment opportunities are just trends and others are pioneer opportunities, where you'll have an opportunity to be on the ground floor with potential for growth. When Facebook went public in 2012, it's I.P.O. (Initial Public Offering) was $39 per share. I invested and now the stock is at $188 per share. My investment grew five times! Make sure you do your research on the industry, market, competitors, government regulations, etc. Know that there is no guarantee.

BUSINESS

Most wealthy people are business owners. Businesses are entities that can build generational wealth. Companies can be passed on to heirs or sold to create an inheritance. Starting and running a business is no easy task, but the payoff can be rewarding. The types of business structures can vary and includes sole proprietor, partnerships, Limited Liability Company (LLC), S Corporation, C corporation, franchise, etc.

One thing I want to point out is that there is a difference between being self-employed and a business owner. The main difference can be mindset. With the growing gig-economy, many people are opting to work for themselves and obtain "gigs" which are really short-term jobs. When considering building a business, it will require systems, structures, and a team, even if it is small to begin with.

The Small Business Administration (SBA.gov) has a plethora of information to help you start and grow your business. They also have several certifications: Women Business Enterprise, Minority Business Enterprise, Minority Women Business Enterprise, DBE, 8A, Hub zone, etc. that if you qualify will give you access to government contracting opportunities. Keep in mind that the government runs and purchases a lot of things, with everything from schools, hospitals, construction, food, professional development, etc. This can open up many opportunities.

Putting Yourself in Position for Business Funding

Whether you are starting a business or attempting to grow your business, at some you may need to have access to capital funding. You may need a business loan or a line of credit or both. Having a favorable credit score is vital for good business financials overall. These steps will help improve your business credit rating as well as maintain a favorable reputation to lenders and investors.

1. **Make Sure Your Business is a Legal Entity**—Your business will not be able to build business credit if it does not have an entity. Consult an attorney about incorporating or form an LLC (Limited Liability Company). Lenders generally will not give a business loan to a sole proprietor because it might be a personal loan in disguise.

2. **Have a Business Address, Telephone Line, Email and Website**—Having a physical location for your company adds credibility for lenders to believe that your company is legitimate. Ideally your office address is not your home address. There are several co-working spaces where you can obtain an address to use at a reasonable cost. Having a business phone line, email address and a website is also essential.

3. **Check Your Business Listings**—Have your company listed under all the necessary agencies under the same exact legal name, phone number and address. It is very important for all your creditors to have you listed under a uniform identity.

4. **Obtain All Necessary Business Licenses, Permits, etc**.—Obtain a business license for your company and if applicable, a license for tax resale in the state, city, or county location of your business. Follow all the necessary regulatory guidelines for running your business.

5. **Organize Financial Statements and Tax Returns**—Be ready to present at least two years of financial statements using the help of a CPA or business owner financial software. It is very important that your business has its own tax ID number. Both federal and state business tax

ID numbers should be enlisted under the same exact legal business name.

6. **Secure Bank References**—How you manage cash flow in your business will be reflected in your banking. A minimum of one bank reference is necessary for your business to establish its score. Ideally your bank account should be active for at least two years, with a good stable balance for three months for it to be in a favorable position for lending.

7. **Obtain At Least Five Trade References**—Your business will need five trade references that have given you a credit account. This may include your suppliers or any firm in which your company has purchased goods from on a regular basis. Make sure to choose references that will give a favorable credit history.

8. **File for Credit that Report to Agencies**—Get three business credit cards that do not have personal links to you and will give business credit reporting agencies their feedback on your company. Dun and Bradstreet is an example of a business reporting entity. Some government contracts require a Dun and Bradstreet number.

When you are ready to apply for business credit you can go to the bank where you have your business bank account or any commercial bank that provides business loans. They will provide you with the list of requirements for funding.

Types and Sources of Funding

SBA Loan—Government backed loan

CDFI—Community Development Financial Institutions (CDFI's)

Connect2Capital.com—A consortium of non-profit lenders ($500 - $4 million)

MyWaytoCredit.com—Access to funding if you are denied from a bank

Crowdfunding—Crowdfunding is the use of small amounts of capital from a large number of individuals to finance a new business venture, typically collected online. Examples are: **Kickstarter.com, Indiegogo.com, GoFundme.com**

Angel Investors—An angel investor is an individual who provides capital funding for a business start-up in exchange for convertible debt (percentage) or ownership equity. Angel investors usually give support to start-ups at the beginning when risks of failing are relatively high.

Venture Capital (VC)—A form of financing that is provided by firms or funds to small, early-stage, budding businesses that are estimated to have high growth potential, or which have demonstrated high growth (in terms of number of employees, annual revenue, or both). It is a type of private equity, investing in these early-stage companies in exchange for equity, or an ownership stake.

Franchise Ownership

Franchises continue to be a growing trend in business. A franchise business is a business in which the owners, or "franchisors", sell the rights to their business logo, name, and model to third party retail outlets, owned by independent, third party operators, called "franchisees". A franchise enables you, the investor or franchisee, to operate a business. You pay a franchise fee and you get a format or system developed by the company (franchisor), the right to use the franchisor's name for a specific number of years and assistance.

The initial investment and start-up costs vary widely for this business type, but some franchises have low initial investment costs and the systems provided make it easier to get up and running. Make sure you do your research on all of the fees involved, opportunity for growth depending on the industry, location, etc. Like any other business, it requires commitment and has a risk of failing.

Some popular franchises are McDonalds, Pinkberry, Domino's Pizza and Dunkin Donuts. A few that have low start-up costs are Fit4Mom, Jazzercise, Chem-Dry, and SuperGlass Windshield Repair.

Real Estate – Home, Investment/Rental Properties

Owning a home can provide benefits such as tax deductions, rental opportunities, and the potential for an increase in value (equity). Also, the sooner you pay it off, the sooner it will free up cash flow, giving you freedom and flexibility to be financially independent during your working career. Also, once it has paid off, this will help your retirement planning because you will have a much lower housing expense when you are no longer working.

Like all investments, there is a risk that your home can lose value or remain the same, but you can always use it to aid in cash flow. I remember when I bought my first house, I was also growing my State Farm business. I really wanted a luxury car, but could not justify buying one at that time, so I rented a room that paid my Mercedes Benz car note. Fast forward to last year, we rented a room through Airbnb on the weekend only and earned $1k per month.

If you are looking to buy a home and do not know where to begin, you can find resources at HUD approved housing counseling agency at **HUD.gov**. They can work with you on the entire process from beginning to end. It is ideal that you meet with them before you meet with a real estate or mortgage agent. They also have access to first-time homebuyer grants, closing cost, and down payment assistance if you quality. There are many different programs depending on the state you live in.

Freddie Mac also has educational programs and resources for first time home buyers, those looking at refinancing or facing foreclosure called **CreditSmart** and **MyHome** at **FreddieMac.com.**

Owning an investment property can also provide additional income, cash flow, and build equity. In one of the properties my husband and I own, the rental income covers the mortgage and expenses and part of our rental housing costs. The tenants will ultimately pay off the mortgage and we will own it free and clear, all while we are living almost free of housing costs. It is important to know that managing rental property requires effort and attention and you, as the landlord, are responsible for maintenance of the property. If you are able to purchase a property with enough rental income to cover all expenses, it may be worth looking into a property manager, depending on the size of the property and the distance from where you reside.

Real Estate Investment Trusts (REIT's)

A REIT is a company that owns, operates, or finances income-producing real estate. REITs provide all investors the chance to own valuable real estate, present the opportunity to access dividend- based income and total returns, and help communities grow, thrive, and revitalize. Similar to a mutual fund as described above, a REIT will have a portfolio of real estate properties in one trust. Returns are paid to the investors. Like any other investment, you must research the REIT, their experience and portfolio before investing.

Passive Income

Passive income includes regular earnings from a source other than an employer or contractor. The IRS says passive income can come from just 2 sources: rental income or a business in which an individual does not actively participate. "Passive" does not mean it will be quick or easy money; you will have to invest time and/or money before you can see a return. Some investments will become turnkey with time, but they all bear a certain risk that has to be calculated and monitored.

Besides some the items mentioned above like real estate rentals, REITs, and dividend paying stocks, there are other ways to earn passive income like writing a book (royalties) or an online course. In these two instances, you create the item once and it is purchased and used over and over again.

Education

With the cost of higher education continuing to rise, planning will be critical for success. Higher education and advanced degrees should be looked at as an investment. Some degrees will have a higher return on investment (ROI) than others. You must count the cost and weigh the pros and cons when making your decision for yourself or a child.

The following sources allow tax deferred growth and strategies to save for college or higher education. They can be used for children or self and some can be transferred to other relatives for education. If you use it for something other than education, you may incur fees. Some will allow the fund to become a retirement account if not used. 529 College Savings Plans and State College Savings Plans like NYSaves.org and Utah Educational Savings are tools you can use to save and prepare for college.

Additional Strategies for College Planning:

If you own a business, there are several ways to strategize to qualify for financial aid and put your child in positions to gain work and business experience. Because you are able deduct pay to workers on your own tax return, if you pay young family members, it moves income out of your high tax bracket and into their lower bracket. Keep in mind FAFSA protects dependent student income up to $6,660 for 2019.

Employing the child also boosts deduction. A dependent child who does not work is entitled to only $1,100 as a standard deduction. One who works gets $350 plus earned income (up to the limit of the usual standard deduction). So, by moving earned income out of your return and into your child's gives you a tax break on your net income.

For family employees under the age of 18, neither the employee nor the employer owes Social Security and Medicare tax. For all of these strategies, please consult with an accountant or tax attorney before implementing.

To obtain cash flow and eliminate room and board expenses, you could purchase a property near campus and turn it into a shared rental for undergrads. Your student can be both one of the tenants and the property manager. This can be a double benefit as they can live rent free and get paid as an employee for managing the property and you all gain the additional tax benefits.

Retirement Planning

Retirement planning is important to ensure you will be able to afford the cost of living in the future. Remember the time value of money example and the importance of covering the cost of inflation in the future. If you work for an employer that offers retirement accounts **(401K, 403B), USE IT!** Your goal should be to max out the amount you can contribute to get the match being offered. This is "free" money. The money is taken out pre-tax, which gives also you tax benefits now and grows tax-deferred. After that, you should have your own **Roth IRA or Traditional IRA** purchased through one of the companies mentioned in the investment section, one you research or are referred to.

If you are self-employed or a small business owner, you are responsible for your retirement and possibly for your employees, so make sure you research **Self Employed Pension (SEP) plans and Simple IRA's.** Do not leave yourself at risk by not preparing for retirement.

Legacy Planning

Generational wealth can be established through creative estate planning including the use of trusts funded by a variety of investment vehicles including life insurance, real estate, businesses, etc. Keep in mind that you do not have to have major assets to establish a financial legacy. My mother never owned a home, but through the benefits from her employer, benefits from her union and life insurance, she was able to leave an inheritance for me, my sister and brother, my oldest daughter, and my nephew. I took part of my inheritance and invested in Facebook, which has since tripled. I also invested my brother's inheritance in a mix of vehicles and earned a 50% return on it.

My other favorite legacy story is about the house we own, where the tenants are paying off the house and part of our housing. My husband's parents, who were immigrants, left the house for him and now our children are reaping the benefits of it and will inherit it after us.

There are many creative ways to create a legacy. No matter where you are on your financial journey, seek the advice of an investment advisor, insurance agent or estate planning attorney to begin to create a plan big or small, because it can happen. Financial victory is yours!

Why is saving, investing or legacy creation important to you?

What will you do first to get started in saving and/or investing? Or increasing your saving or investing?

Who will hold you accountable? When will you meet with them?

What else do you need to get started? (Contact us for help vanessalindley.com)

Who wants to be a Millionaire?

10 steps to becoming a millionaire:

1. Develop a written financial plan and follow it

2. Automate savings

3. Live below your means—stop spending mindlessly—stick to your spending plan

4. Lay off the credit—unless it is giving you leverage for an investment

5. Make your money work for you—do the math

6. Act like a Boss—start your own business

7. Get professional advice—financial coach, investment advisor, financial planner

8. Invest in multiple streams of income

9. Act like a millionaire—your mindset matters

10. Spend time with millionaires—check your circle of influence

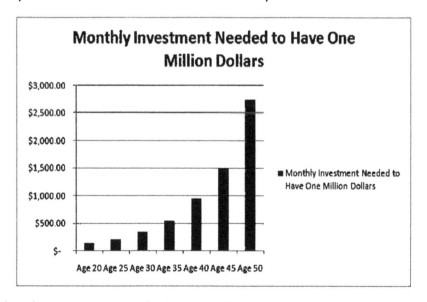

This chart is assuming about an 8-10% return, which requires strategy

As you see from the chart, starting early will require less of a monthly investment, as opposed to starting later. At 20 years old you may only need $100 invested consistently in an investment that over the long run produces an average return of 8-10% (acknowledging highs and lows over time). If you start later, say at 45 years old, it will require more of a monthly investment of $1,500 for the same results.

Wherever you are on your saving, investing, or wealth building journey, know that it is never too late to get started. Don't be dismayed, there are multiple ways to accumulate assets. Start with your goal, devise a plan, practice, ask for help and do not quit! Financial victory is possible!

STEP 5

MANAGING FINANCES AND FAMILY

"She goes to inspect a field and buys it; with her earnings she plants a vineyard. [17] She is energetic and strong, a hard worker. [18] She makes sure her dealings are profitable; her lamp burns late into the night."
— Proverbs 31:16-18

FINANCES AND FAMILY

Home Economics

Our family dynamics have a major impact on our finances, how we spend or save money, how we plan, and what we can do with our money. I recommend all households treat their finances like a business. Your household finances are your personal economy. As your family changes or grows, it can be challenging to keep things in order and stick to a plan. The best way to achieve financial victory in this area is to include all family members in the goal setting and planning process.

Having Family Planning Sessions and Weekly Meetings to Discuss:

- Individual goals and family goals
- Allowance/spending money
- Grocery shopping
- Family vacations
- Clothing
- Entertainment
- Finances for Two

If you are married or planning to get married, financial planning should start immediately, if it hasn't already. Many couples will get physically intimate before they get financially intimate. You must have "courageous conversations" about money early and often to ensure you all are on the same page or at least working toward a middle ground.

I recommend thinking about how you can live off of one income, even if both people work. This can help your household in the long run, whether you decide to have children or not. It can offset the two-income trap, help with long-term savings, wealth building, and offset major emergencies like a health-related crisis and employment lay-offs. As a couple you have to decide what accounting strategy works best for you, who pays what bills, how many accounts to have, whether they are separate or combined. The most important thing to do is to communicate often, plan, track, and adjust as needed. (Are you starting to see a trend here?)

Coming to an agreement on a unified budget and having both people follow it can be challenging at times. If you remember from step #2, everyone has their own money habits, beliefs, and money scripts, which can make agreeing challenging. Working with a neutral third party like a financial coach may help.

Baby Makes Two or Three or More

Preparation and planning are always going to help families with children. Planning the family schedule, meals, activities, and even snacks. Things like snacks and impulse purchases can derail a budget. Children have a strong influence on family purchases and various studies say the spending power of children are in the billions or trillions.

Sometimes we can plan our spending and sometimes we are caught by surprise. Either way, we have to make the necessary financial adjustments and be diligent in planning. When choosing among all of the financial obligations in raising children, there will always be trade-offs in your choices. For example, if you send your child to costly activities such as summer camp or tutoring, you may not be able to take a big vacation that year.

A key strategy is to be mindful of how and why you are choosing to make purchases for your children. Pay attention to the emotions that come up when spending money on your children beyond their basic needs. What emotions are being triggered in you? Guilt? Power? Are you trying to make up for a void in yourself or in your life? Are you carrying your own childhood emotions into your decisions for your children? These are hard things to consider, but important to be aware of. This will give you power to be intentional about how you want to raise your children and the financial legacy you want to leave with them.

Another consideration are the external influencers that impact your decisions that come from community, circle of influence and culture. For example, do an assessment of your values and motivation in deciding to enroll your children in certain activities. The pressures of a community can inform your decision because you hear things like "everyone's daughter or son is doing it." There are times when it is important for social and community, other times it may not. You get to choose, but make sure you pause and are aware of why you are making the decision.

There is also a factor of whether the activity is worth the investment. For example, if you are investing all of your discretionary income in gymnastics hoping your child will be the next "Gabby Douglas," or all of her/your friends are doing it, but your child is not that interested in the sport or are not that competitive, you may want to consider another investment of your family's time and money.

As my family grew, there were many things that I was not prepared for because I just did not know. So many people gave me tips on feeding, Mommy and Me activities, early childhood development, but no one talked about money and planning. That is why I recommend researching and planning for the costs of the items in the chart below, as far in advance as possible. Calculating the total costs monthly, yearly and the total investment (total number of times you spend on this item) can be helpful in forecasting.

Item	Monthly or Yearly	Total Investment
Formula		
Diapers		
Day Care		
Childcare (date night, meetings)		
Private School tuition		
Extra-curricular activities (dance, gymnastics, soccer, karate, language, arts, STEM)		
Summer Camp		
College		
Clothes		
Entertainment		
Snacks and treats on the go (all year round)		

These items do not always make it to a budget template, and I know it is necessary for families to identify and include them in their budget. It will bring both awareness and intention to what you value and how you spend your money on your children.

Allowance—The Hybrid Approach

Most parents do not know where to begin when it comes to allowance. Some give allowance for chores; others give it for being a member of the family. I prefer a hybrid approach, where you give your child a set amount of money each week as allowance. This should not be directly tied to any chore or job. It should be made clear to them that as part of the family, they are expected to do certain daily chores like make their bed, put up their dishes, and clean up their toys.

Children who want to earn additional money can do other jobs around the house, above and beyond the basics like bathing the dog, cleaning the windows, or raking the leaves. This hybrid approach sets clear expectations and gives your child real money to learn from.

When you are ready to start an allowance program with your child, be as clear as possible. "Daughter, because you are getting older and there are things that you want to buy, we're going to start giving you an allowance. That means each week we will give you $7, which you will divide into your three jars." I recommend the "Save, Spend and Share" system. You decide how to divide the money among the three; for simplicity you can just divide it equally.

I suggest taking them to the bank to open a savings account and make deposits, if possible. Give them their own card, have them check their balances and plan their spending goals. There are many ways to handle allowance, the lessons about money they learn, and the savings habit are what is most important. So, do what's best for your family.

Allowance Guidelines:

- **How much?** How much money should you give your child? That is up to you and depends on your personal financial situation. A general rule of thumb is to pay $1 for each year. So, your five-year-old gets $5/week, at six years old they get $6/week, and so on.

- **Be consistent.** If you are planning to give your child a set amount of money each week, make sure you give them the same amount on the same day.

- **Establish spending boundaries** on what they are expected to buy with their own money, and what you will pay for.

- **Cash is king.** By giving your children allowance in cash and coins it makes it easier to teach your them about money when it's tangible. Also, the visualizing of the money growing in the jars or piggy bank can be influential.

- **Make allowance positive.** If your child misbehaves, don't tell them that you'll take away their allowance. This is most children's first hands-on experience with money; you don't want it to cause them anxiety. This could have an impact on their future relationship with money.

You want to focus on leaving legacy of a healthy relationship with money for your children. Regardless of your income or wealth, see money as a tool to provide for your family's needs and wants. Work on managing your emotions around spending and becoming a model for your children. As you continue to work and grow in this area, continue to teach your children lessons they can apply throughout their life.

Family Binder

Every family should have what I call a family binder. This binder should include all financial accounts and policies in a binder, file, or an online file. You may want to have it locked in a file cabinet, fireproof box and/or have online password that you share with your partner, spouse, significant other or confidant.

Family Binder Content

- Insurance policies
- Bank accounts
- Employment benefits – insurance, retirement
- Social Security benefits statements

- Deeds and mortgage statements
- Investment accounts
- Wills, living wills, healthcare proxies, trust documents
- Passwords to online accounts

Courageous Conversations

As you and your family prepare this binder, there should be more "courageous conversations" happening. You should be discussing what you all have in terms of your financial life, where the documents are, who owns what, etc. Take this time to talk about life, the big and little things.

You may need to have these conversations with your parents and/or your children. They can be uncomfortable and, in some families, and communities they may be taboo, but they have to start happening for the protection of the people you care about. Your family can achieve financial victory!

Who do you need to have a "courageous conversation" about money with?

What do you want to say to them? What do you want to ask them?

When will you schedule a time to talk?

Prepare your version of a family binder and share it. *Set a date to have it completed and schedule a date for the family meeting, this will give you a deadline to accomplish it.*

What do you need help with in this area? *(Contact us at vanessalindley.com)*

STEP 6

PROTECTING ASSETS

"She is clothed with strength and dignity,
and she laughs without fear of the future."
– Proverbs 31:25

PROTECTING ASSETS

In step #4 I focused on accumulating assets, this step will focus on how to keep and protect your assets. Protection is a key aspect of the prosperity cycle and extremely important on your path to financial victory!

What Can't You Afford to Lose? Take a moment to think about that. These are things that without them we would feel the effect financially. For example, I cannot afford to have my credit score go to low, because it could affect my employment, housing, and insurance opportunities. It could also cause me to pay more for goods and services.

What are some things you can't afford to lose?

What will you need to protect your family and assets? There are several ways to protect your family and assets. You can reduce/eliminate the risk, retain (keep or self-insure) it or transfer the risk to an insurance company. For example, one thing most people cannot afford to lose is their health, but many people don't think of health as an asset until they or a loved one becomes ill and can no longer work and/or the medical bills start to come in. One way to reduce the risk of becoming ill is to eat healthy foods, stay active and get regular medical check-ups.

Another example of a form of protection is having an emergency savings. This is a way to retain or self-insure the risk of experiencing a financial emergency, like a car breaking down. Without an emergency savings, you could risk having to borrow for the repair and incurring interest and debt. You could also have no resources and be unable to get to work without your car and have no way to repair it, putting your source of income at risk as well.

The most commonly known form of protection is insurance. There are a variety of types of insurance that offer different forms of protection depending on your risk. It is important to speak to an insurance professional or financial advisor to help you plan and prioritize the appropriate policies for you. You must shop around for the best company and policy that meets your needs. I recommend that you review your risks and protections yearly, to accommodate changing life circumstances.

My husband, at 53 years old, unexpectedly had to have open heart surgery, a triple bypass. This caught us off-guard; he had not had any prior incidences, was not on any medication and had actually been dancing at a party two days before he unknowingly began having mild heart-attacks at home. It was not until this incident that we realized how fortunate we were to have medical and disability insurance as my husband was unable to work for three months. Prior to this, we may have complained about our insurance premiums, but after this we were thankful for all of the benefits it provided like a visiting nurse, a physical therapist and all of the new medication he had to begin taking.

He was also fortunate to have short-term disability through his employer that provided 80% of his income during the time he was unable to work. Not sure how we would have survived without these benefits. I know insurance can be expensive, so I advise families to meet with their employer benefits person first to see if they can maximize those benefits first because they tend to cost less out of pocket. After that they should meet with a reputable insurance person who could help them create a protection plan that feels comfortable and can continue to build on it as their financial situation changes.

Types of Insurance

- **Life**—Protects the income of the insured, covers funeral costs and can create an inheritance

- **Health**—Provides health insurance coverage to allow insureds to get check-ups and treatments

- **Car**—Protects your vehicle from accidents or the insured if they are at fault

- **Home/Renters**—Protects the insured for their personal property from theft and damage and home for damage as well as liability protection if sued

- **Disability**—Provides income protection if the insured is unable to work for short- or long-term periods, depending on the policy

- **Long Term Care**—Provides protection of assets when the insured needs long-term care in a facility or at home

Will, Living Will, Healthcare Proxy, Power of Attorney, Trusts

Many people are not aware of the need for a will, living will, or healthcare proxy. These can protect your wishes as it pertains to your life and your assets while you are alive and after you are gone. The will can spell out how you want your remains to be finalized and how you want your assets to be distributed. This matters even if you do not have a lot of assets. You can seek an attorney or go online for more information on this.

A living will spell out how you want your affairs handled while you are still alive, but unable to handle your affairs. In most cases you will also designate someone to have the "power of attorney," which gives them the power to act and sign on your behalf. The healthcare proxy advises the doctors, hospitals and all involved what type of medical treatment you prefer i.e. no blood transfusions, do not resuscitate, etc.

A trust is a tool that allows a third party, or trustee, to hold assets on behalf of a beneficiary or beneficiaries. Trusts can be arranged in many ways and can specify exactly how and when the assets pass to the beneficiaries. You will need an estate planning attorney to set one up for you. It is best to do these things while you are healthy and before a crisis. Things can change in an instant, so it is best to get started as soon as possible.

If you want to begin the process on your own, you can; there are online resources to assist you in creating wills, living trusts and life insurance:

- Nolo.com

- LegalZoom.com

- Tomorrow.me

Make a Commitment:

I will have the "courageous conversation" with the people who are important in my life on_____. I will tell them what my financial goals and final wishes are. I will select appointees and complete all necessary estate documents by _____.

Credit Protection

In our current economic system, your credit score in an asset and must be protected. Your credit/score can affect your housing, employment, transportation, insurance and investment opportunities. It is important to protect it through financial planning (Step # 1) and regular monitoring through one of the following credit repositories.

- Annual Credit Report
- My Fico
- Equifax
- Trans Union

- Experian
- Credit Karma
- Quizzle
- Credit Sesame

Identity Protection

Besides your credit report and public records like bankruptcy, there are other entities called consumer reporting companies, collecting information on how you conduct your financial life (e.g., employment, tenant, banking, insurance claims, utilities and retail). For example, when you apply for job or housing rental, you sign a document giving the entity permission to do a "background check."

They are accessing and reviewing this information to learn about your past behaviors at your prior work or prior home rental. I recommend you get a copy of your own report to make sure the reports are accurate. You are entitled to one free copy per year and can dispute any discrepancies. The reports can be found on Consumer Financial Protection Bureau.

The reports include:

- Employment
- Tenant
- Banking
- Personal property insurance

- Medical claim history (MIB)
- Utilities
- Retail

The full list of consumer reporting companies can be found online at ConsumerFinance.Gov: (https://www.consumerfinance.gov/consumer-tools/credit-reports-and-scores/consumer-reporting-companies/). The site provides instructions on how to correct any errors.

Personal Financial Risk Assessment

Circle (yes) or (no) to the following questions, add the total of each to assess your risk level.

1. I have three to six-months cash emergency fund.   Yes No

2. I have pulled my credit report and monitor it regularly.   Yes No

3. I have an inventory of my assets (bank accounts, personal   Yes No

4. Property, home, investments, retirement accounts, etc.)   Yes No

5. I have adequate car/home/renters' insurance.   Yes No

6. I have adequate life insurance to provide for my family.   Yes No

7. I have disability insurance.   Yes No

8. Do you know how much you will need to retire and how much you can safely withdraw from your assets in retirement?   Yes No

9. I have a will, power of attorney, living will and healthcare proxy.   Yes No

10. My beneficiary designations for my life insurance and retirement accounts are up to date and match my estate plan.   Yes No

11. I have an ID Protection plan in place.   Yes No

Number of "NO" Answers	Risk
0 – 1	Low
2 – 3	Moderate
4 or more	High

What area of protection are you most vulnerable?

What will be your first step to providing adequate protection?

If you need to seek a financial expert (financial coach, estate attorney, CPA, insurance agent) set a date to do so.

STEP 7

GIVING BACK

"In everything I did, I showed you that by this kind of hard work we must help the weak, remembering the words the Lord Jesus himself said: 'It is more blessed to give than to receive.'"
— Acts 20:35

Vanessa Lindley

GIVING BACK

As you work to achieve financial victory and becoming a "Legacy Maker," you are working to create a legacy that will outlive you. On your journey, you cannot forget about living a life of gratitude, giving back, and paying forward. Giving provides a life of abundance. Most wealthy people began with tithing and giving. There is a principle that states, as you give you shall receive.

There are many ways to give back or pay forward, through tithing, donations, and volunteering. These are personal choices, but each add tremendous value in your life and to your legacy. If tithes and offerings are something you value, you must include them in your budget and overall financial plan. Life is more than money.

Tithing and Offerings

- 10% + of your spending plan

Donations

- To causes you care about—justgive.org, give.org, guidestar.org
- Can be tax deductible—make sure you confirm if this is important to you

Volunteering

- Volunteering your time is worth a lot, time is money

What ways can you plan to start giving back to causes you care about?

Why is this important to you?

THE LEGACY MAKER PLEDGE

1. I will be my authentic self at all times.

2. I will commit to a growth mindset.

3. I will stay in the moment and be present.

4. I will refrain from negative self-talk.

5. I will surround myself around people who are positive and encouraging.

6. I will commit to doing one thing per day to move me closer to my goals.

7. I will pursue my passion with persistence.

8. I acknowledge that my legacy is more than money.

9. I will be thankful for where I am while I am on my path to fulfilling my purpose.

10. I will help others on my journey.

Make a pledge out loud to yourself, with your accountability partner or your family. Commit to create the legacy you desire!

NEXT STEPS

"My favorite things in life don't cost any money. It's really clear that the most precious resource we all have is time."
– Steve Jobs

Whether you have read this book cover to cover in one sitting, one step per day or week, you will need to take action on your learning. Here is 30-day plan for you to complete to continue to deepen your learning and focus on your journey to financial victory!

30-DAY PLAN
Interview one older person in your family and ask him/her about his/her belief about money. Discuss how these beliefs have played out in/affected his/her life.
Have a conversation with your spouse/partner and/or children about money. (Whatever you feel you need to talk about.)
Complete all worksheets in workbook (especially spending plan).
Track your spending for two weeks (online, in a notebook, keep receipts) and tally. Discover your spending leaks and make adjustments, then track again for two weeks.
Write your will, living will and healthcare proxy.
Talk about estate planning and your legacy with the people who are important to you (you get to decide).
Hire a Financial Coach – VanessaLindley.com.
Sign up for updates– VanessaLindley.com.
Meet with a financial advisor to determine product needs.

ACCOUNTABILITY

A success strategy to help you reach your financial goals is to have some form of accountability. Circle the one you want or need the most and contact them ASAP! It is victory time!

- Associate
- Friend

- Financial Coach
- Wealth Building Club

PREPARING WITH WORK WITH
A FINANCIAL COACH

If you are interested in working with a financial coach, there are some things you can do in preparation:

Gather Information

1. Financial resources

   - Income sources
   - Expenses
   - Debt
   - Bank accounts
   - Insurance policies
   - Credit score(s)

2. Explore Emotional resources and hurdles (Covered in Step 2)

   - Feelings about spending and saving
   - Relationship with money
   - Intra-family communications

Assessment

While the main point of the assessment is about determining where you are today so you can get where you want to be in the future, the process might surface some basic financial hurdles/issues that would need to be addressed (possibly through a variety of sources) before you could move forward. Key questions for consideration include:

- **Does your income meet expenses?**

- **Is there a dependency on credit cards and/or other high-interest debt?**

- **Is your credit report correct?**

- **Are you insured against the right risks?**

This is where we begin, and we ride with you on your journey to reaching your financial goals and help you live the life you want to live while leaving a lasting legacy! You can achieve financial victory!

ABOUT THE AUTHOR

Vanessa A. Lindley is the CEO of The Lindley Consulting Group LLC, also known as the "Legacy Maker." She is a dynamic speaker, financial coach, consultant, and author. Her mission is to help individuals, families and organizations understand the financial impacts of daily life and create a lasting legacy. Her focus is in the areas of personal finance, financial behaviors and wealth building.

Lindley Consulting Group is a Minority- and Women-Owned Certified Business. Vanessa is an alumna of the Goldman Sachs 10K Small Business program. In her combined experience in the Financial Services, Insurance and Real Estate industries, she has been a State Farm Agent, where she held Series 6 and 63 and insurance licenses and received numerous awards for outstanding sales. As a real estate investor, she has owned and managed multi-million-dollar properties.

As an author, Vanessa has written "Achieve Financial Victory: 7 Ways to Win with Your Money," and contributed to several curricula, "Realizing the American Dream," "Financial Coaching: Helping Clients Reach their Goals" and "Delivering Effective Financial Education for Today's Consumer."

With over twenty-five years' experience her client list includes Citi, Chase, Columbia University, St. John's University, the National Urban League, the Congressional Black Caucus Foundation, Freddie Mac, NeighborWorks America, State of New York Mortgage Association, New Jersey CDC, among other organizations and small businesses. On her mission to help people recover from financial crisis, Vanessa has responded to assist the victims of Hurricane Katrina in New Orleans, and Hurricane Sandy victims in NY and NJ in similar efforts.

Vanessa is a member of Jack and Jill of America, Inc., feeds the homeless, donates to various back to school efforts, and volunteers for any opportunity to give back. She has been recognized by the Queens Chapter of the Alpha Kappa Alpha Sorority, Inc. as Community Leader of the Year, and a 2019 Women of Wall Street. Her dedication to making an impact on the world is only superseded by her dedication to her family. She is a wife, a mother of three girls and became a guardian for her younger brother after the death of her mom.

FOR MORE INFORMATION CONTACT:

The Lindley Consulting Group LLC

Ph: 646-404-7007

Email: info@vanessalindley.com

VanessaLindley.com

LindleyConsultingGroup.com

Twitter, IG, LinkedIn @vanessalindley

facebook.com/LindleyConsultingGroup

Made in the USA
Middletown, DE
30 January 2021